Row Row Row Your Boat

ROW ROW ROW YOUR BOAT

AS TOLD AND ILLUSTRATED BY
IZA TRAPANI

SCHOLASTIC INC.

New York Toronto London Auckland Sydney
Mexico City New Delhi Hong Kong

ISBN 0-439-19896-8

12 11 10 9 8 7 6 5 4 3 2 1   0 1 2 3 4 5/0

Printed in the U.S.A.   08

First Scholastic printing, May 2000

Text was set in 18-point Tiffany Medium.
Book production and design by *The Kids at Our House*

For Pat and Margaret,
Johnny, Daniel, Helen, and Anna,
May you share many merry adventures!

Row row row your boat
Gently down the stream
Merrily, merrily, merrily, merrily,
Life is but a dream.

Row row row your boat
Happy as can be
Sunshine glowing, off and rowing
With your family.

Row row row your boat
Stroke and follow through

Fumbling, flailing, oars go sailing—
What a clumsy crew!

Row row row your boat
Row with all your might

Rocking, bashing, water splashing
Better hold on tight!

Row row row your boat
Look ahead to find

Beavers damming, logging, jamming
Left you in a bind!

Row row row your boat
Stop to have a munch
Chomping, snacking, slurping, smacking
What a noisy bunch!

Row row row your boat
Better row to shore

Raining, hailing, wind is wailing
Hear the thunder roar!

Row row row your boat
Find a place that's dry
Scurry, scuttle, hide and huddle
Till the storm blows by.

Row row row your boat
And away you go

Skies are clearing, sunset nearing
Homeward bound you row.

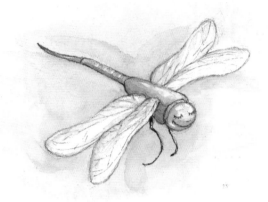

Row Row Row Your Boat

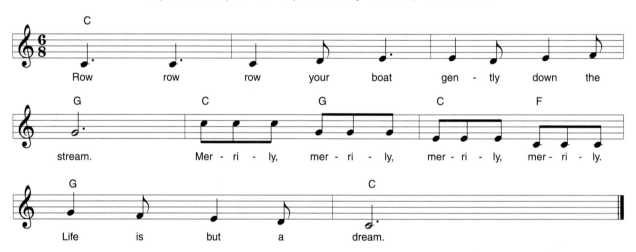

Row row row your boat gen - tly down the stream. Mer - ri - ly, mer - ri - ly, mer - ri - ly, mer - ri - ly. Life is but a dream.

2. Row row row your boat
Happy as can be
Sunshine glowing, off and rowing
With your family.

3. Row row row your boat
Stroke and follow through
Fumbling, flailing, oars go sailing—
What a clumsy crew!

4. Row row row your boat
Row with all your might
Rocking, bashing, water splashing
Better hold on tight!

5. Row row row your boat
Look ahead to find
Beavers damming, logging, jamming
Left you in a bind!

6. Row row row your boat
Stop to have a munch
Chomping, snacking, slurping, smacking
What a noisy bunch!

7. Row row row your boat
Better row to shore
Raining, hailing, wind is wailing
Hear the thunder roar!

8. Row row row your boat
Find a place that's dry
Scurry, scuttle, hide and huddle
Till the storm blows by.

9. Row row row your boat
And away you go
Skies are clearing, sunset nearing
Homeward bound you row.